# the BAD GUYS

## in

## MISSION UNPLUCKABLE

· AARON BLABEY ·

# the BAD GUYS

SCHOLASTIC INC.

in

MISSION
UNPLUCKABLE

# NEWS FLASH!

## PANIC AT THE DOG POUND!

We interrupt this program to bring you a breaking news story.

**TIFFANY FLUFFIT** is our reporter on the scene. Tiffany, what can you tell us?

CHUCK MELON  6 NEWS

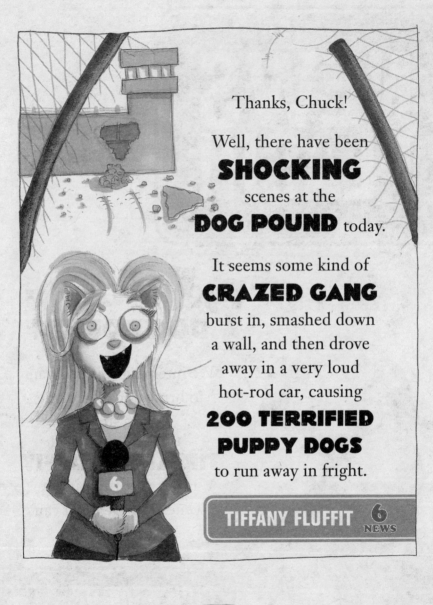

Thanks, Chuck!

Well, there have been **SHOCKING** scenes at the **DOG POUND** today.

It seems some kind of **CRAZED GANG** burst in, smashed down a wall, and then drove away in a very loud hot-rod car, causing **200 TERRIFIED PUPPY DOGS** to run away in fright.

**TIFFANY FLUFFIT** 6 NEWS

I have with me **MR. GRAHAM PLONKER**,
Chief of Dog Pound Security.

Mr. Plonker, how would you describe these
# MONSTERS?

Uh . . . well . . . it all happened so
fast, but . . . I'm pretty sure there
were four of them . . .

I mean, there was definitely a **WOLF**.

EXCLUSIVE FOOTAGE!

A really *mean*-looking wolf, with pointy teeth.

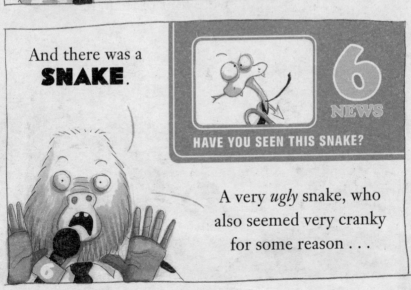

And there was a **SNAKE**.

HAVE YOU SEEN THIS SNAKE?

A very *ugly* snake, who also seemed very cranky for some reason . . .

Uh, then there was a **YOUNG LADY** ...

PRETTY GIRL? OR DEADLY SHARK?

... or possibly a gigantic **SHARK**. It was hard to tell which ...

Oh yeah, and there was also some kind of nasty little fish.

MUTANT SARDINE ON THE LOOSE!

Maybe a **SARDINE**.

Not sure.

But, Mr. Plonker, would
you say that these
*villains* seemed . . .

## DANGEROUS?

Oh yes, Tiffany. They're
dangerous, all right.

In fact, I'd say we are dealing
with some *serious* . . .

LIVE FROM THE DOG POUND **6** NEWS

# CHAPTER 1 •
# OK, LET'S TRY THAT AGAIN

What's that guy talking about?
We **SAVED** those puppy dogs!
It was a
# RESCUE!
We're the **GOOD GUYS** here!

AND FOR THE LAST TIME,
I AM **NOT** A SARDINE!
# I'M A
# PIRANHA!

See, Wolf? No one is **EVER** going to believe we're good guys. I'm getting out of here before the cops come looking for us.

Oh, **NO** you don't, Mr. Snake! We're not going to quit now. We're just getting started.

Don't forget **HOW GOOD** it felt to
rescue those dogs!

All we need to do now is make sure that
everyone can **SEE** that we're **HEROES**.

We just need to do something
**SO AWESOME** that the whole
world will sit up and take notice!

What did you have in
mind, Mr. Wolf?

You want us to break
into a chicken farm?

Chickens?

Did you say . . . *chickens*?

A chicken farm?
But that little chickie
looks happy. She doesn't
need to be rescued . . .

Oh, really?

Well, take a look INSIDE
Sunnyside Chicken Farm, fellas.

# 10,000 CHICKENS!

Stuffed into **TINY** cages!

**24** hours a day!

With **NO** sunlight!

And **NO** room to run and play!

But that's awful!
That's the worst thing
I've ever heard!

What are we waiting for?!

WE NEED TO SET THOSE
LITTLE CHICKIE-BABIES

**FREE!**

Let's go! Let's go! Let's go!
Let's go! Let's go! Let's go!
Let's go! Let's go! Let's go!
Let's go! Let's go! Let's go!

**LET'S GO!**

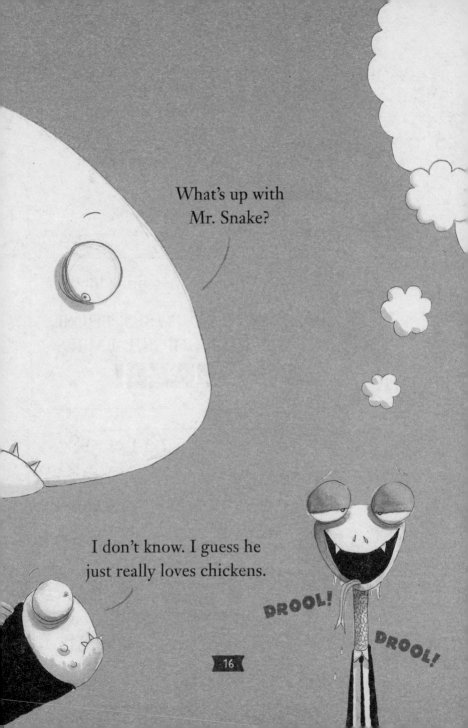

What's up with
Mr. Snake?

I don't know. I guess he
just really loves chickens.

DROOL!

DROOL!

16

Well, *hellooooo* . . .

Are you OK, man?

Huh?

DROOL

Oh yeah . . . sorry.
I was just thinking that chickens are delicious—I mean, *DELIGHTFUL*— and I think we need to save them all **RIGHT NOW**.

Oh, if only it were that simple, my friend. But I'm afraid I have some bad news . . .

Sunnyside Chicken Farm is

# IMPOSSIBLE

to break into!

It's a **MAXIMUM SECURITY CHICKEN FARM** with **STEEL WALLS** that are 30 feet high and 8 feet thick!

There are **NO WINDOWS** and all the doors are **HEAVILY GUARDED.**

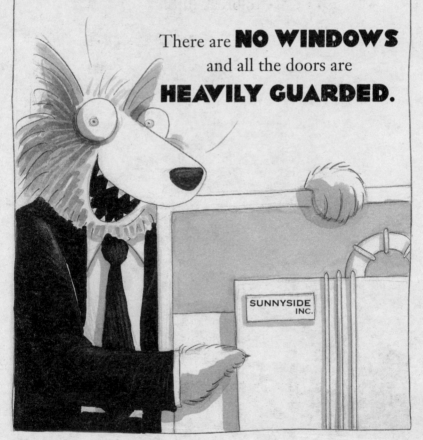

SUNNYSIDE
INC.

And even if you *did* get inside, you'd be caught instantly because . . .

If you touch the FLOOR, an **ALARM** goes off!

If you touch the WALLS, an **ALARM** goes off!

And if you walk into the LASER BEAMS, an **ALARM** goes off!

• FLOOR ALARMS

• WALL ALARMS

• LASER ALARMS

Did you say
## LASER BEAMS?
Why are you even showing us this, *chico*? We don't have the skills to pull off a job like this!

No, we don't.
But I know a guy who does.

Who?

# · CHAPTER 2 ·
## the
## FREAKY GEEK

Hey, dudes! It's totally awesome to meet you!

Aieeeeee!
**RUN** *CHICOS*! It's a
# TARANTULA!!!

I'm sorry about this, Legs. I don't know what's wrong with them.

Aw, it's cool. Happens all the time.

**LEGS?!**

You *know* this monster?!

What were you thinking, bringing a tarantula into our clubhouse?

*. . . Can't breathe . . .*
*spider . . .*
*Mommy . . .*
*Mommy . . .*
*I want my mommy . . .*

*Mr. Shark!* Pull yourself together!
You guys should be ASHAMED of yourselves!
**LEGS** is just like us.
He's a GOOD GUY with a BAD reputation.

Aw, thanks,
Wolfie.

He's **DANGEROUS,** man.

Yeah!
And why isn't he
wearing any pants?

I don't do pants, dude. I like to feel free.

*. . . can't breathe . . .*
*no pants . . .*
*freaking . . . out . . .*

Okeydoke.

Legs? Why don't you show them what you can do?

OK. Let's start with something simple.

TAP! TAP! TAP! TAP! TAP! TAP! TAP!

ACCESS: GRANTED
Name: MR. SNAKE
Status: Very Dangerous
Action: Do Not Approach

Hey! That's my police file!

Geez, they don't like you very much, do they?

But **NOBODY** can access that! There's no way you can hack into their system. That's the toughest security there is!

Yeah, it *is* kind of tricky.

TAP! TAP!

TAP!

TAP!

TAP!

TAP!

TAP!

But it's worth it just to see you smile, Mr. Snake.

Ta-da!

That's **IMPOSSIBLE!**

Not for a **SUPERHACKER** like Legs! He's a computer **GENIUS**. And he has a plan that will get us inside that chicken farm.

Thanks, Wolfie. But first, I'd better put this back the way I found it. We are good guys, after all . . .

. . . and I wouldn't like to get us in trouble. Sorry, Mr. Snake. You're *dangerous* again, I'm afraid.

Hey!

This is **SO** cool, guys! I'm so happy to be part of the team. And I bet by this time tomorrow, we're totally going to be **BESTIES!**

*. . . spider . . .*

*. . . with no pants . . .*

*. . . on my head . . .*

**FAINT!**

**SPLAT!**

Hey, *chico.*
I got one word for you—
*pants.*

# · CHAPTER 3 ·
# MISSION, LIKE, TOTALLY IMPOSSIBLE

OK, dudes, I took your advice and found myself some clothes. What do you think?

I can still see his
**BIG FURRY BUTT.**

Cut it out,
Piranha.
Just listen
to him.

**OK.**

To get you guys inside
Sunnyside Chicken Farm,
all I need to do is hack into
their main computer and
switch off all the alarms.

**BUT**

there's a problem . . .

The security is
## SO HIGH
that I can't do it from here.

I need you guys to plug
## THIS THING
into their computer,
so I can access it.

Once you do that, I can
SHUT IT ALL DOWN
and get you to those
chickens.

Wait a minute. You're telling us that you can hack into my police file, but you **CAN'T** get into a CHICKEN FARM without our help?

Yeah. It's WEIRD. This is one SCARY chicken farm, dude.

But if it's so scary, how do we get to the computer? Wolf said there's no way into the building!

Well, there is **ONE** way.

But it sure isn't easy . . .

There's a
**SMALL HATCH**
on the roof.

You'll need to go
through the hatch
and **DROP**
150 feet on a rope
to the computer
below. Once you
get to it, **JUST
PLUG ME IN**.

# BUT!

If you touch the
WALLS or the
FLOOR, the
**ALARMS** will
go off and you'll
get caught.

That's it?
That doesn't sound so bad.

I'm not finished.

Once you plug me in, you have to climb back up the rope, crawl through this **AIR VENT** and follow the tunnel to the CHICKEN CAGES.

ROOF

AIR VENT

Like I said, that doesn't sound so bad.

## I'M STILL NOT FINISHED.

You see, before you reach the chicken cages, you'll come to the **LASER BEAMS**. And if you touch one, the alarms will go off.

Oh, and they'll zap you. And they *really* hurt.

LASERS

→ AIR VENT →

But why are the lasers still on? I thought you were going to shut down all the alarms.

I will.
The **OTHER** alarms will be off.

But the **LASER ALARMS** can only be turned off by hand. You have to flick a switch once you're inside.

So . . . we just switch them off?

Yep.

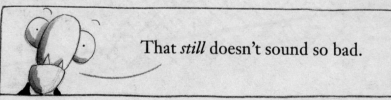

That *still* doesn't sound so bad.

That's because I'm **STILL NOT FINISHED!**

The switch is on the OTHER SIDE of the laser beams, so you have to GO **THROUGH** THEM to reach it!

CHICKENS
THIS WAY

You finished yet?

Uhhh . . . yep.

Good! Because
that sounds

# LOCO!

There's **NO WAY** we
can pull this off, man!

Oh yes, we can!

But **ONLY** if we work as a **TEAM!**

So, Snake and Piranha—
you guys are coming with ME!

We are going to **GET INSIDE**,

plug **THIS THING** into the computer, and

**GET TO THOSE CHICKENS!**

This is going to be

**GREAT!**

But . . . what about me?

You're going to be working with me, Big Guy.
It's OUR JOB to get these guys in and out of there safely!
Isn't this awesome? You and I are going to SPEND A
**LOT** OF TIME TOGETHER!

*Oh . . . that's . . .
great . . . but . . .
I think . . .
I'm going . . .
to cry . . .*

No time for tears, Mr. Shark.

# WE'VE GOT CHICKENS TO SAVE!

# • CHAPTER 4 •
# DOWN THE HATCH

Hey, what are you guys doing
all the way over there?

Hey, Tarantula! What's with the stupid suits?

*Shhh!* Not so loud, Mr. Piranha. These suits are GREAT! They'll keep you cool and make you really hard to spot.

# PLUS!

Each suit has a microphone and earpiece, so we can all talk to each other.

# GOT IT?

Hey, Wolf, do you really promise there'll be chickens down there?

It's a **CHICKEN** FARM! Of course there'll be chickens. Why are you so worried about that?

Oh, no reason.

I just really **LOVE** chickens, man.

They're so nice to eat— I mean, they're so nice to *MEET*.

Yeah . . .

You DO understand that we're here to SAVE the chickens, don't you?

 Uh-huh.

 And you wouldn't try to **EAT** any chickens, would you?

 Uh-uh.

 Hey! Can we just DO THIS? My jumpsuit is chafing.

OK. Mr. Shark? You
know what to do . . .

Gently lower us on the count of three.

ONE . . .
TWO . . .

OK. OK. OK. Well, the walls are a *little* closer than I expected.

Mr. Shark! Whatever you do, make sure you lower us *SLOWLY*.

I hear you.

Do you need a hand, Big Buddy?

BOING!

EEEEEEEEE E E

FOOF!

Whoa. That was close.

# ¡AY, CARAMBA!

Mr. Wolf?
Has anyone ever told you that
your face looks like a **BUTT?**

What?

Oh. Sorry. My mistake.

Hey, look! The computer!
I think I can reach it . . .

He didn't see us.
Why didn't he see us?

Are you kidding?
WE GET
OUT OF
HERE!

*Shhh!* I don't know.
He must have really bad eyesight.    SHARK?!
Um . . . OK . . .    ABORT!
Any suggestions on what we do now?    ABORT!
PULL US
UP NOW!

Okeydoke . . .

NO! WAIT!

Look what he's eating, *chicos*. That's a sardine sandwich.

I think I have an idea.

Piranha? You're not going to do anything crazy, are you?

"Crazy" is what I bring to the party, *chico*. Wish me luck . . .

Piranha! No!

This was a one-way ticket, *chico*.

 WHAT? We can't just leave you behind!

 You have to, *hermanos*. There is no other way.

Go and save those little chickens, man. Save them for **ME!**

Wolf! Snap out of it!
SHARK! Pull us up!

You got it.

Hurry up, man.
Just get in the vent, will you?

Look at him
down there!

What a brave
little guy!

He sacrificed
himself for us.

*Adios,*
*chicos.*

Yeah, yeah. Let's do this.
I'm starving—I mean,
I'm *STARTING* to want to
save some chickens. Yep.

You're
right.
We
should
go.

*Adios,*
Mr. Piranha.

Stay safe.

Easy for you
to say, baby.

# · CHAPTER 5 ·
# MIND THE GAP

See, Mr. Snake? This is what I've been talking about—without Mr. Piranha, we would **NEVER** have made it this far. **THAT'S** what being on a team is all about. **COOPERATION.**

Yeah, yeah, yeah, that's *so* interesting, but WHERE ARE THE CHICKENS, man?

Just up ahead, I'd say.

This bit has been a lot easier than I thought. I really don't know what all the fuss was ab—

eeEEEEEE!

Geez.
If I were you,
I'd try not to
look down.

DANGER!
150-FOOT
DROP

ALL I CAN SEE
IS **DOWN!**

Hey! I have an idea. Why don't you stay here?

I'll go and eat— I mean, *GREET* those chickens.

Noooo! I'm slipping! I . . . can't hold on. You have to . . . help me . . .

Really? That's a bit annoying.

**ANNOYING?!** IF YOU DON'T HELP ME, I'M GOING TO **DIE!**

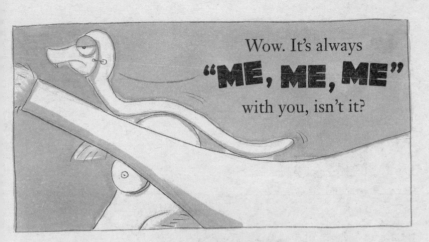

Wow. It's always **"ME, ME, ME"** with you, isn't it?

SLIP!

Oh no!

SLIP!

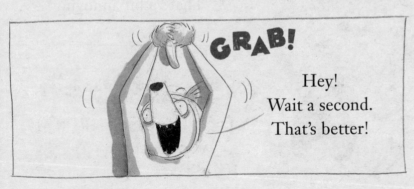

GRAB!

Hey!
Wait a second.
That's better!

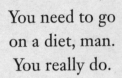
You need to go on a diet, man. You really do.

Now, let's think.

What do we do?

We're trapped.

It's not just ME that's trapped. And it's not just YOU. It's **US**.

We're trapped as a **TEAM**. So we need to get out of this as a **TEAM**.

I'VE **GOT** IT!

# · CHAPTER 6 ·
# LET'S START OVER

That's not good.

Piranha?
Can you hear me?

Mr. Shark? Is that you?

I'm about to be a monkey's lunch here, man.

You sit tight, Mr. P.
I'm coming to get you.

BOING!

Can I help,
**BIG FELLA?**

*Really . . . scared . . . of . . . spiders . . .*

Uh-huh. And why is that?
It's OK, you can tell me.

OK, well . . .
you're **FREAKY** to look at because
you have **TOO MANY EYES** and
**TOO MANY LEGS**
and I'm **SO** creeped
out by you that
**I MIGHT
THROW UP!**

But . . . I'm sorry if that
sounds rude.

 It's OK.

No, really. I feel terrible saying
that. You must think I'm awful.

 No, that's OK.
You seem like a nice guy.
But can I ask you one little thing?

Yes, of course.

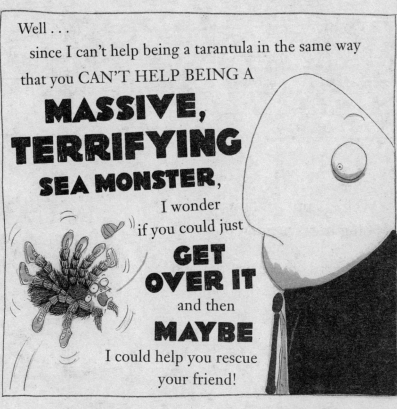

Well . . .

since I can't help being a tarantula in the same way

that you CAN'T HELP BEING A

# MASSIVE, TERRIFYING SEA MONSTER,

I wonder
if you could just

## GET OVER IT

and then

## MAYBE

I could help you rescue
your friend!

Um . . . OK.

I'm so sorry. That was really uncool.

It's OK. That's good advice.

Well . . . um . . . how are we going to rescue that piranha?

I've heard you're pretty good at disguises. Is that right?

I have my moments.

OK, well, I'm REALLY good at making stuff. So why don't we work together?

OK.

But what kind of disguise is going to get me inside a chicken farm?

Why don't you pull the feathers out of those pillows there, Mr. Shark, and I'll tell you my idea.

# · CHAPTER 7 ·
# TRUST ME, I'M A SNAKE

Oh no! Look at those laser beams! I'll **NEVER** get through!

I think we have a problem.

*Ooooooh no, no, no, no.* There's no problem—I'll fit through those lasers. I'll just have to handle this one **ALONE.**

Are you sure?

Oh, ABSOLUTELY.
I'll just wriggle my way across and have a chicken feast—I mean . . . I'll get those chickens **RELEASED.**

Yeah.
*Released.*
Heh heh.

But you'll switch off the lasers when you get across?

Yeah, yeah, sure.

You take your time, little buddy!

**YOU ROCK!**

I'm just SO proud of these guys.

WHISTLE
WHISTLE

Geez, it's been fifteen minutes.

Are you OK over there, Mr. Snake?

Aha! He's done it.

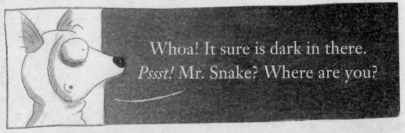

Whoa! It sure is dark in there.
*Pssst!* Mr. Snake? Where are you?

Oh, there you are!
Is everything OK?

*Urghugh.*

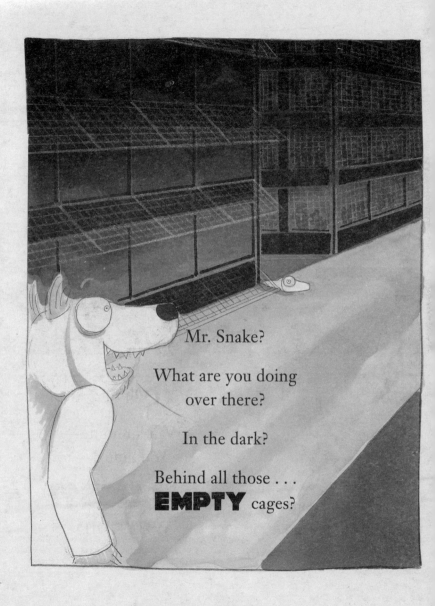

Mr. Snake?

What are you doing over there?

In the dark?

Behind all those . . . **EMPTY** cages?

*Gnnughgagh.*

You sound funny, man.
Are you OK?

*Sgllurrr!*

Oh no.

Wait a minute—
You didn't—

# SNAKE?!
WHAT DID
YOU DO?!!

Oh, I don't think so.

Snake, you are *not* going to ruin this plan. No, you are not.

Huh?

GRAB!

NO.
YOU.
ARE.
NOT.

I TRUSTED YOU! How could you do something so awful?

I'm a SNAKE, man. What did you expect?

**NO,** Mr. Snake. YOU ARE A GOOD GUY. And you're not leaving this building without 10,000 healthy and happy chickens—EVERY SINGLE FLUFFY ONE OF THEM. **ARE YOU FEELING ME?**

# · CHAPTER 8 ·
# WHOLE LOTTA CHICKEN

Who knows? But let's get it back down to the cages.

Oh, sorry! I interrupted your lunch . . .

Aw, that's OK. I can eat on the run.

Hey, *chico*. What's up?

MUNCH!

Clive! Your sardine is alive!

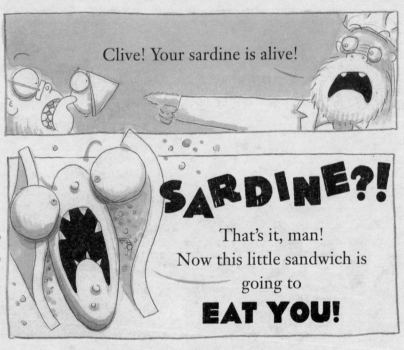

SARDINE?!

That's it, man!
Now this little sandwich is
going to
EAT YOU!

Wow! I barely recognized you.

 Yeah, I know.
I'm good at disguises.

WHOOP! WHOOP! WHOOP!

**OH NO!** They've set off the alarm!

WHOOP! WHOOP! WHOOP!

But Wolf and Snake will be trapped!

Guys! It's Legs! Get out of there! They're coming for you!

WHOOP! WHOOP! WHOOP!

We're not leaving without our *chicos*.

Or our chickens.

We've opened the cages, but they won't run. What's wrong with these stupid chickens?

They're scared.

Of what?

OF THE CREEP WHO TRIED TO **EAT THEM!**

I couldn't help it.

I'm sorry.

Yeah, well, "sorry" won't help us now, Mr. Snake.

What are we going to do? The chickens are terrified.

They need someone to **FOLLOW**.

They need someone to **TRUST**.

They need . . .

Wow. That's one big chicken.

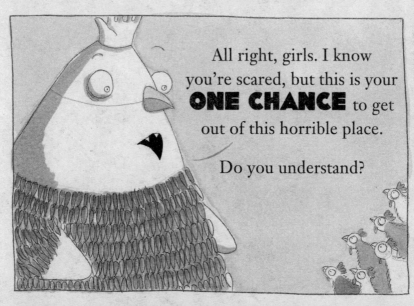

All right, girls. I know you're scared, but this is your **ONE CHANCE** to get out of this horrible place.

Do you understand?

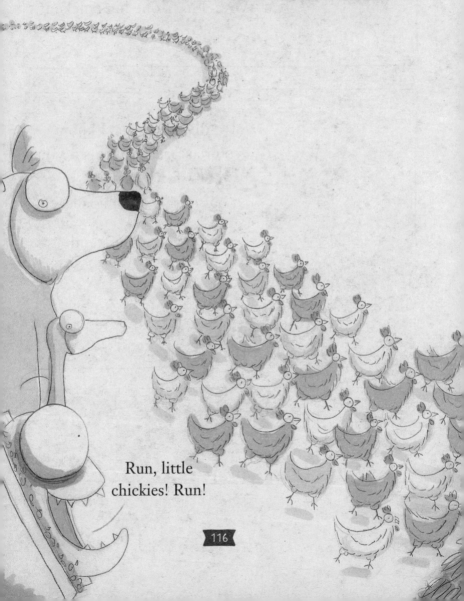

GOOD.

Run, little chickies! Run!

# THEN LET'S GET OUT OF HERE!

Mr. Piranha!
You're here!

Are you OK?

I'm completely coated
in mayonnaise.

Oh. I see.

It's not too bad, actually.

I kind of like it.

We're **TRAPPED!**

This is the **END!**

My chickens will **NEVER** be free!

Throw me at him!
It's your only chance!

That's the craziest thing
I've ever heard!

This is my chance to do
some good, Mr. Wolf.

But—

THROW ME NOW OR THESE CHICKENS WILL NEVER BE FREE! DO IT!

And don't miss. GOT IT?

Got it.

Hi. Let's play a game. The first person to open the door doesn't get bitten by a snake.

You win.

Now, can I ask you to please lock all the guards in behind us after we leave?

Yes, we do.

Oh, and if you don't, I **WILL** find out where you live and you **WILL** find me in your bed in the middle of the night.

Do we have a deal?

Marvelous!

BOING!

See? You're not the only Good Guy around here . . .

I knew it! I knew it! I knew it!

OK. Less hugs. More escaping.

# · CHAPTER 9 ·
# WHAT A TEAM

I am so proud of you guys!

**10,000** chickens are free
because of **YOU!**

I think we're starting to get the hang of this hero thing, fellas.

And that means you, too, Mr. Snake.

OK, Huggy Bear. Let's not make a great big hairy deal out of it.

Aw, sure thing, you old grouch! Let's get out of here . . .

But . . .

Oh yeah. While I was waiting for you guys to get back, I fitted it with **MONSTER TRUCK** tires and a **JET ENGINE**. I hope you don't mind?

We don't mind!

And I noticed that you seemed a little cramped in there, Mr. Shark, so I've modified your seat. If you don't like it, I can always put it back the way it was.

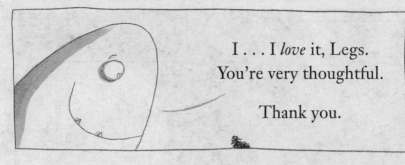

I . . . I *love* it, Legs.
You're very thoughtful.

Thank you.

Anytime, Mr. Shark.
Anytime at all.

*I'm breathing.*
*It's all good.*
*I'm breathing.*
*It's all good.*
*I'm breathing.*
*It's all good.*

**SQUEAK!**

Hey! Did
anybody else
hear that?

CRACK!

SQUEAK!

SUNNYSIDE INC.

Hmmm.
It seems to be coming from that
**CREEPY OLD HOUSE**
next to the chicken farm that we . . .
somehow didn't notice. Perhaps it's
a chicken that's lost its way?

I didn't know chickens
could squeak . . .

134

Nope. My mistake.
There's nothing here. It's empty.

Well, no. It's not
*completely* empty . . .

Look!

*Awww!* Look at the widdle guinea pig! What are you doing here all alone?

I think he's named Marmalade. Cute, isn't he?

MARMALADE

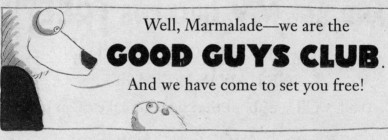

Well, Marmalade—we are the

# GOOD GUYS CLUB.

And we have come to set you free!

You take care, little Marmalade. ENJOY YOUR FREEDOM!

See you, little guy.

Good . . . guys?

137

# GOOD GUYS?

And just because they call themselves
GOOD GUYS, they think they can

# BREAK INTO MY CHICKEN FARM AND SET MY CHICKENS FREE?!

AND THEY THINK THEY CAN
GET AWAY WITH IT?

Well, we'll see about that. I shall make them pay.

Oh yes . . .

# I SHALL MAKE THEM PAY! HE HE HE HE HE HE! HE HE HE HE!

The **BAD GUYS** are doing some **GOOD** ... whether you **WANT THEM TO OR NOT**.

Don't miss their first **heroic** adventure—*breaking every last dog out of the pound!*

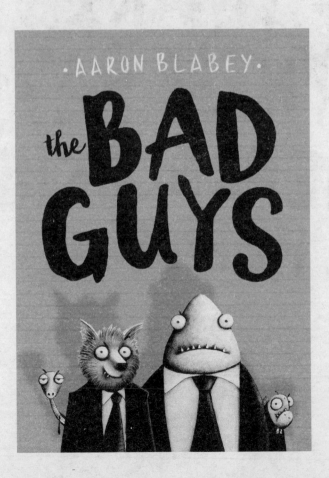